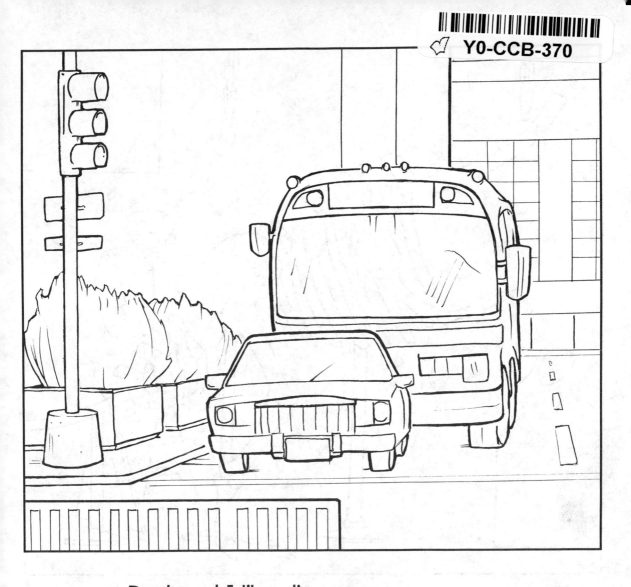

Dad and I like dinosaurs.

We rode the bus to the museum

to see a new set of dinosaur bones.

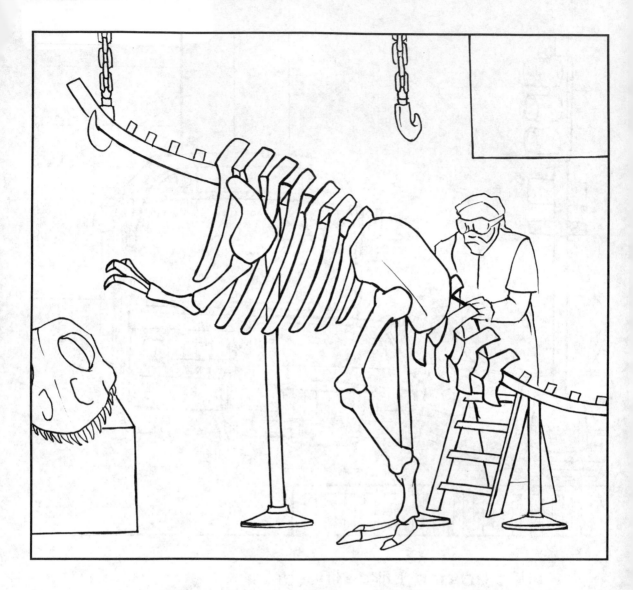

The workers were putting the bones together.

They put the bones on a big pole with bars.

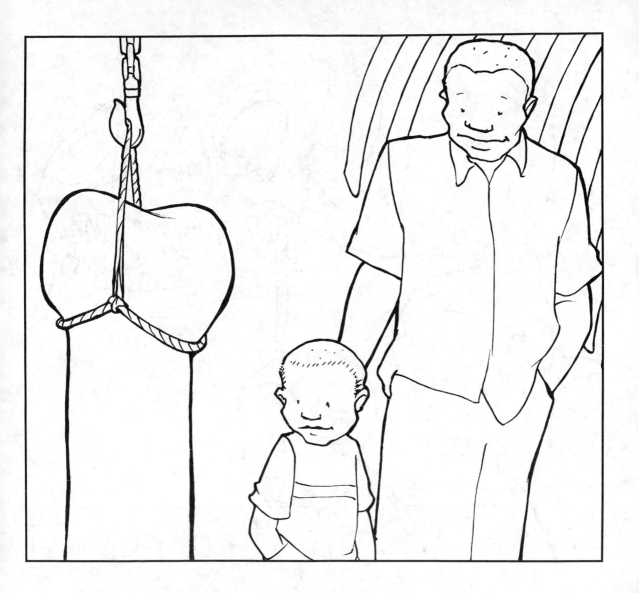

Each bone had to be put in place.

The big bones were lifted with ropes.

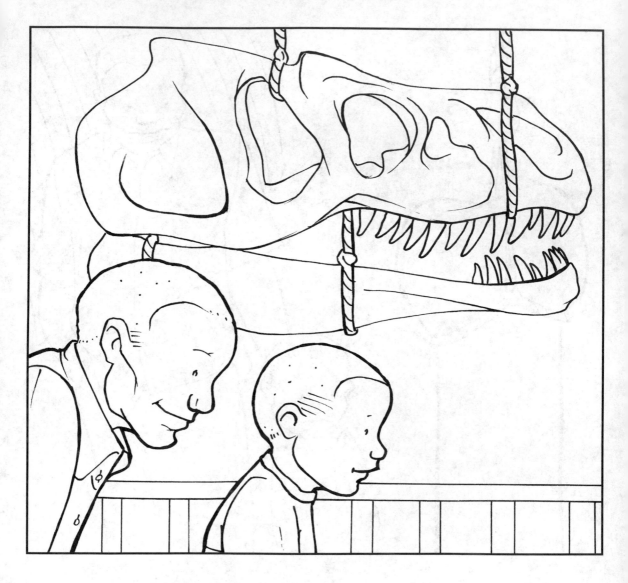

"Look at the skull," said Dad.

We could see the holes for the eyes and nose.

"Look at those teeth!" I said.

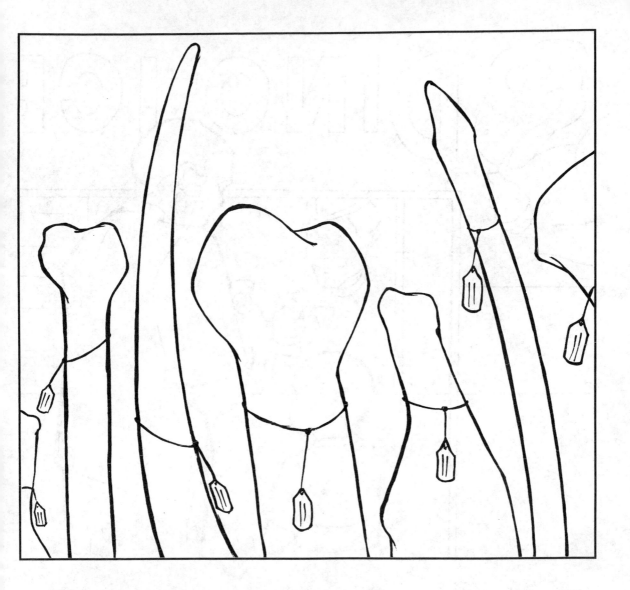

There were so many bones.

It would take days to put them together.

"It's getting late," said Dad. "We have to go."

We got an ice cream cone to eat on the way home.

"I hope we can come back when the bones
are all put together," I said.
Dad smiled. "We will," he said. "We will!"

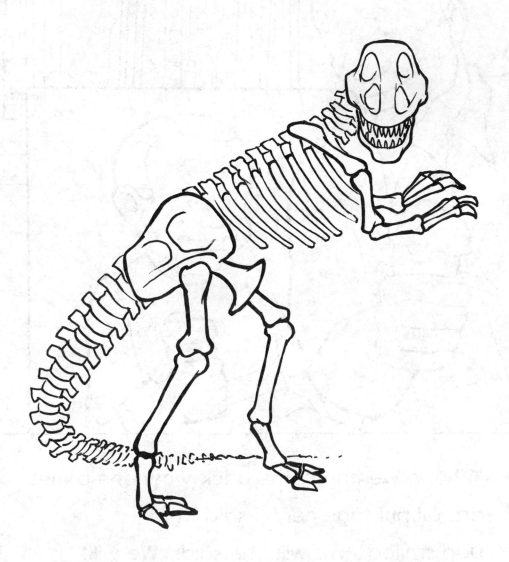